Key Vocabulary for a Safe Workplace

MIAMI-DADE COMMUNITY COLLEGE
HOMESTEAD CAMPUS
500 COLLEGE TERRACE
HOMESTEAD. FL 33030-6009

Harry Ringel

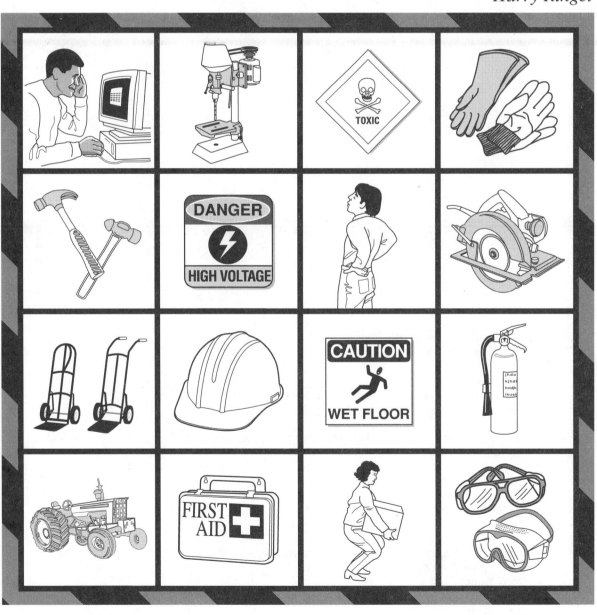

Key Vocabulary for a Safe Workplace
ISBN 1-56420-175-9
Copyright © 2000
New Readers Press
U.S. Publishing Division of Laubach Literacy International
Box 131, Syracuse, New York 13210-0131

Printed in the United States of America
9 8 7 6 5 4 3

Director of Acquisitions and Development: Christina Jagger
Developmental Editor: Paula Schlusberg
Copy Editor: Judi Lauber
Designer: Patricia A. Rapple
Illustrators: Linda Tiff, Luciana Mallozzi
Cover Designer: Kimbrly Koennecke

Contents

UNIT 1

Workplace Safety Basics

Unit 1 presents basic safety warnings and equipment to help you work more safely.

You will learn about
- common workplace warning signs and why these warnings are important
- clothing and protective gear that you can wear for safety at work
- basic equipment and workplace features that help provide safety for workers
- first aid materials at work that you can use in case there is an accident or health problem

As you study these lessons, think about these questions:
- What warning signs and safety equipment do you see in your workplace?
- What warning signs do you know from other places?
- What protective gear do you and your co-workers wear?
- How can you use the language and information in these lessons to work more safely?

Safety Signs and Warnings

Study and Learn

Here are common warning signs that you can see in the workplace.

Do Not Enter

No Smoking

Do Not Touch

High Voltage

Watch Your Step

Caution: Wet Floor

Keep Aisles Clear

Keep Area Clean

Restricted Area

Do Not Operate Machine

No Food or Drink

Authorized Personnel Only

Which Sign?

Check the best warning sign for each situation.

1. Only hospital workers wearing special equipment can go into an X-ray room safely.
   ____ **a.** Keep Area Clean   ____ **b.** Restricted Area

2. Workers have to move large boxes through a warehouse when they stock the shelves.
   ____ **a.** Keep Aisles Clear   ____ **b.** Authorized Personnel Only

3. A broken factory sewing machine can hurt a worker who tries to use it before it is repaired.
   ____ **a.** Do Not Operate Machine   ____ **b.** Watch Your Step

4. A janitor has just mopped the floor of an office building.
   ____ **a.** Keep Area Clean   ____ **b.** Caution: Wet Floor

5. A worker must repair loose wires on a telephone pole.
   ____ **a.** Do Not Operate Machine   ____ **b.** High Voltage

6. The grill in a restaurant kitchen is turned on all day, so the surface is very hot.
   ____ **a.** Watch Your Step   ____ **b.** Do Not Touch

7. At an auto body shop, the doorway to the office is higher than the floor in the work area.
   ____ **a.** Watch Your Step   ____ **b.** Do Not Enter

8. The cleaning workers have a lot of chemicals that can catch fire easily.
   ____ **a.** Do Not Enter   ____ **b.** No Smoking

9. Some laboratory equipment requires special training for safe use.
   ____ **a.** Watch Your Step   ____ **b.** Authorized Personnel Only

10. A computer assembly worker has to keep the tools very clean.
    ____ **a.** No Food or Drink   ____ **b.** Do Not Touch

What Is the Danger?

Write the best warning sign to go with each picture.

No Smoking	Keep Aisles Clear	Keep Area Clean	Watch Your Step

1.

2.

3.

4.

Work Safely

Why is the sign important for the worker in each item? Write your reasons.

1. "No Food or Drink" is important for an assembly-line worker because

   _____

2. "High Voltage" is important for a factory worker because

   _____

3. "Do Not Operate Machine" is important for a worker in a machine shop because

   _____

4. "Watch Your Step" is important for a construction worker because

   _____

What about You?

What warning signs do you see where you work? Where are the signs located in the workplace? Why are they there? Fill in the chart.

Sign	Location	Reason for Warning
High Voltage	electrical box	danger of shock

LESSON 2 Personal Protective Equipment

Study and Learn

Here are common items that people wear at work to protect different parts of the body.

hard hat

hair net

apron

back brace

gloves

respirator

face shield

dust mask

earplugs/
earmuffs

rubber boots/
work boots

work shoes/
safety shoes

safety glasses/
goggles

What Does It Protect?

Write the items that protect each part of the body. Use the words on page 10.

1. These protect the eyes: _____

2. These protect the head: _____

3. These protect the feet: _____

4. These protect the lungs: _____

5. These protect the ears: _____

6. These protect the hands: _____

Protect Yourself

Match each workplace danger with the equipment that protects against the danger. Some items have more than one answer. Protective equipment may be used more than once.

Danger	Equipment
_____ 1. cuts on the hands	a. goggles
_____ 2. dust or chemicals in the air	b. earplugs
_____ 3. chemicals splashing the body	c. safety shoes
_____ 4. falling objects	d. back brace
_____ 5. loud machine noise	e. face shield
_____ 6. objects hitting the eyes	f. gloves
_____ 7. sore or strained back	g. hair net
_____ 8. chemical fumes	h. respirator
_____ 9. hair getting caught in machines	i. rubber boots
_____ 10. wet floors	j. hard hat
_____ 11. working near flames or fire	k. apron

What Should They Wear?

Write the protective items that the workers in the pictures need to wear. There is more than one item for each picture.

earmuffs	gloves	work shoes	apron	work boots
hard hat	dust mask	earplugs	goggles	face shield

1.

_____

2.

_____

3.

_____

4.

_____

Work Safely

Check the correct reason for each statement.

1. Some factory workers wear hair nets because
   _____ **a.** their hair can get pulled into a machine
   _____ **b.** it is important to look neat on the job

2. Auto body repair workers often wear earplugs because
   _____ **a.** noise from power tools can damage their hearing
   _____ **b.** repair shops can be very cold in winter months

3. Machine workers usually wear goggles because
   _____ **a.** they can see better and do their work more exactly
   _____ **b.** sparks or pieces of metal can fly into their eyes

4. Some farmers wear respirators because
   _____ **a.** insect-killing chemical sprays can hurt their lungs
   _____ **b.** respirators feel very comfortable on the face

5. Nursing assistants often need to wear a back brace because
   _____ **a.** they can hurt their backs moving patients
   _____ **b.** they look more important if their backs are straight

What about You?

Think about the personal protective equipment covered in this lesson.
Do you use any of these items in your work? Does anyone you
know use them? If so, which ones are used? For what job are they
used? Why? Create a chart on separate paper.

Protective Equipment	Type of Job	Reason
ear plugs	factory	loud machines
goggles	factory	sharp objects flying around

Around the Workplace

Study and Learn

Here are common safety devices that you can find in many workplaces.

guardrail

fire alarm

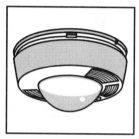
smoke detector

sprinkler

fire extinguisher

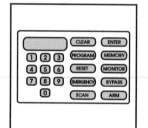
security system

emergency lighting

first aid station

emergency exit

first aid kit

fire escape

eyewash station

What Should Be There?

Complete each sentence with the name of the safety item that is needed.

fire extinguisher	guardrail	eyewash station
security system	sprinklers	fire escape
emergency lighting	fire alarm	first aid kit

1. Outside a large factory, a _____ leads down to the ground from all floors.

2. There is always a _____ in a fast-food kitchen, where cooks work all day with hot oil, grills, and ovens.

3. Many factories have an _____ in case workers splash chemicals in their eyes.

4. During a power failure, _____ shows workers in an office building how to reach the exits.

5. At night, a _____ sounds an alarm if a thief breaks into a workplace.

6. At a construction site, a _____ keeps workers from falling into the excavation.

7. If a fire begins in a clothing store, _____ on the ceiling put out the fire right away.

8. Every workplace needs a _____ in case a worker gets injured or sick on the job.

9. If a fire starts in a workplace, the sound of the _____ will tell workers to leave the building.

What Is the Danger?

What safety problems do you see in the picture? Write the name of the problem on the line.

---

a. empty first aid kit
b. locked exit door
c. blocked emergency exit
d. broken guardrail

1.

_____

3.

_____

2.

_____

4.

_____

Do's and Don'ts

Look at the pictures on page 16. Write a rule to correct each problem.

1. (first aid kit) Always _____

_____

2. (emergency exit) Never _____

_____

3. (guardrail) Always _____

_____

4. (exit door) Never _____

_____

What about You?

Do you see any safety items from this lesson at your workplace? If so, explain why each item is important.

1. _____ is important because _____

_____

2. _____ is important because _____

_____

3. _____ is important because _____

_____

First Aid
for the Workplace

Study and Learn

Here are basic items that you can find in many first aid kits.

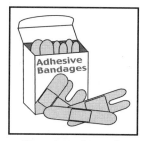

adhesive bandages

eyecup/
eyewash

hot water bottle

ammonia/
smelling salts

splint and sling

syrup of ipecac

gauze pads/
gauze bandages

antiseptic:
spray/ointment

adhesive tape

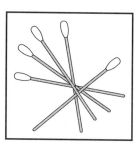

cotton swabs

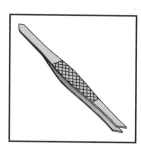

tweezers

ice pack

What to Use?

Check one first aid item that each worker can use.

1. A landscaper is stung by a bee. What can she use to remove the stinger?

    _____ **a.** tweezers   _____ **b.** cotton swab

2. A painter hurts his ankle in a short fall from a ladder. What can he use to stop the swelling?

    _____ **a.** sling   _____ **b.** ice pack

3. A food preparation worker cuts his thumb while slicing meat. What can he put on the wound to prevent infection?

    _____ **a.** hot water bottle   _____ **b.** antiseptic

4. A janitor splashes cleaning chemicals in her face. What can she use to get the chemicals out of her eyes?

    _____ **a.** eyewash   _____ **b.** cotton swab

5. A cook spills boiling water on his arm. After he bathes the arm with cool water, what can he put on the burn?

    _____ **a.** gauze pad   _____ **b.** hot water bottle

6. A computer operator has not eaten all day and faints. What can his co-worker use to revive him?

    _____ **a.** smelling salts   _____ **b.** antiseptic

7. A construction worker falls and breaks her arm. What should she use until she can get to a hospital?

    _____ **a.** gauze bandages   _____ **b.** splint and sling

8. If you eat or drink something poisonous, call the Poison Control Center and find out if it is safe to use this product.

    _____ **a.** ammonia   _____ **b.** syrup of ipecac

9. A child gets a small cut on her knee at day care. What can the daycare worker use to clean the cut?

    _____ **a.** cotton swabs   _____ **b.** tweezers

10. What can the daycare worker put on the child's cut to keep it clean?

    _____ **a.** an adhesive bandage   _____ **b.** an ice pack

Apply First Aid

Write the name of the first aid item that the worker needs in each picture.

| syrup of ipecac | adhesive bandage | hot water bottle | eyewash/eyecup |

1.

_____

3.

_____

2.

_____

4.

_____

What Does It Do?

Match each first aid item to its function.

First Aid Item

_____ 1. smelling salts

_____ 2. splint

_____ 3. antiseptic

_____ 4. syrup of ipecac

_____ 5. eyecup

_____ 6. tweezers

_____ 7. adhesive tape

_____ 8. gauze pad

_____ 9. ice pack

_____ 10. cotton swab

_____ 11. eyewash

_____ 12. hot water bottle

_____ 13. adhesive bandage

_____ 14. sling

Function

a. holds liquids for rinsing an eye

b. provides heat to relax sore muscles

c. holds bandages on the body

d. revives a fainting victim

e. is used to apply medication

f. helps pull out small, sharp objects

g. covers burns, cuts, or small wounds

h. supports an injured arm or hand

i. reduces swelling of a sprained joint

j. covers a small cut

k. holds a broken bone straight

l. is used to rinse an eye

m. induces vomiting (makes a person vomit)

n. prevents infection in cuts

What about You?

Does your workplace have a first aid kit or a first aid station? If so,
what first aid items are available?

_____   _____   _____

_____   _____   _____

Unit 1 Review

Read each situation below. Write the letter of the correct safety item
on the line.

a. adhesive bandage	**d.** Caution: Wet Floor	**g.** apron	**i.** earmuffs
b. fire extinguisher	**e.** Watch Your Step	**h.** gloves	**j.** back brace
c. emergency exit	**f.** smoke detector		

_____ **1.** Jorge has just mopped the hallway. He puts out this sign to warn people.

_____ **2.** A small fire starts in the kitchen where Bea works. She uses this to put out the fire.

_____ **3.** Noise from power tools bothers Soo. She blocks the noise with these.

_____ **4.** Lynn carries a lot of boxes. This sign reminds her to be careful on stairs.

_____ **5.** Miriam cuts her arm. She puts this on to stop the bleeding and cover the cut.

_____ **6.** Smoke fills the front of Tony's store. He uses this to leave the building.

_____ **7.** Kay works in a photo lab. She protects herself from chemical spills with this.

_____ **8.** Charlie loads wooden crates of fruit onto delivery trucks. He wears these to protect his hands from cuts and splinters.

_____ **9.** The crates that Charlie loads are very heavy. He also wears this to support his back when he lifts the crates.

_____ **10.** Tina has one of these in every room of her company, to give a warning in case there is a fire.

UNIT 2

Safe Use of Tools and Machinery

People use many different tools and machines in their jobs. These tools and machines can make work easier, but there are also risks.

Unit 2 presents common hand tools, small power tools, and large machinery. It includes some of the basic parts that make these tools and machines operate. It also includes some important safety features on many tools and machines.

Maybe you do not use a tool or machine yourself. But you need to understand the possible risks and ways to avoid those risks.

As you study these lessons, think about these questions:

- What tools and machines do you use at work or in other activities?
- What tools and machines do your co-workers use?
- What do you and your co-workers do to be safe around tools and machines?
- How can you use the language and the information in these lessons to work more safely?

LESSON 5 Hand Tools

Study and Learn

Here are common hand tools that people use in many different jobs.

hand drill

hammers

mallet

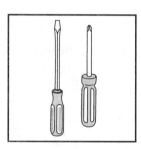
screwdrivers

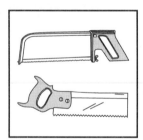
hacksaw/
handsaw

pinking shears/
kitchen shears

pruning shears/
garden shears

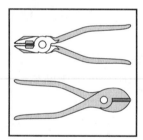
wire cutters/
snips

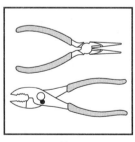
pliers

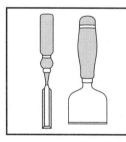
chisels

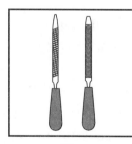
files

wrenches

Which Tool to Use?

Check the tool that each worker can use to do the job.

1. A gardener is cutting branches from bushes and trees.
   _____ **a.** pruning shears   _____ **b.** pliers

2. A mechanic is removing a flat tire from a car.
   _____ **a.** wrench   _____ **b.** hammer

3. An electrician is removing old cable.
   _____ **a.** wire cutters   _____ **b.** kitchen shears

4. A builder is removing small pieces from a brick.
   _____ **a.** hacksaw   _____ **b.** chisel

5. A furniture maker is making holes in a table top before she attaches the legs.
   _____ **a.** hand drill   _____ **b.** file

6. A plumber is attaching a new showerhead to a pipe.
   _____ **a.** screwdriver   _____ **b.** wrench

7. A metalworker is cutting and shaping a piece of tin.
   _____ **a.** snips   _____ **b.** handsaw

8. A cabinetmaker is smoothing the edge of a piece of wood.
   _____ **a.** file   _____ **b.** chisel

9. A dressmaker is cutting a piece of cloth.
   _____ **a.** pruning shears   _____ **b.** pinking shears

10. A maintenance worker is replacing a doorknob.
    _____ **a.** wrench   _____ **b.** screwdriver

11. A cabinetmaker is fastening doors onto the frames of kitchen cabinets.
    _____ **a.** screwdriver   _____ **b.** hammer

What Are the Dangers?

Study these safety rules for using hand tools. Write the letters of the rules that each worker should follow.

a. Keep work area neat.	**d.** Handle tools carefully.
b. Use the right tool.	**e.** Work in a well-lighted area.
c. Keep tools sharp.	**f.** Wear protective equipment.

1.

_____

2.

_____

3.

_____

4.

_____

Be Safe

Look again at the pictures on page 26. Write at least one piece of safety advice for the workers in each picture. Circle **Always** or **Never** to fit the advice. Give a reason for the advice.

Picture 1. Always/Never _____

because _____

Picture 2. Always/Never _____

because _____

Picture 3. Always/Never _____

because _____

Picture 4. Always/Never _____

because _____

What about You?

Do workers use any of the hand tools from this lesson where you work? If so, which ones? What jobs do they help workers do? What are the safety risks in using the tools for those jobs? Create a chart on separate paper.

Tool	Job(s)	Risk(s)
hammer	maintenance	could hit fingers

Small Power Tools

Study and Learn

Here are common power tools used in many different workplaces.

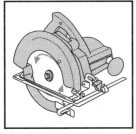
circular saw

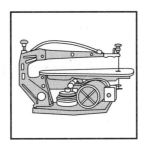
jigsaw

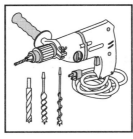
power drill

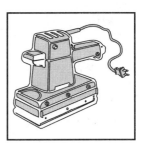
sander

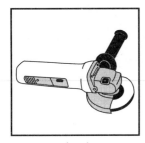
grinder

welding torch

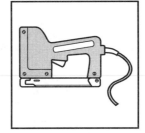
staple gun

glue gun

power
screwdriver

paint sprayer

vacuum cleaner

buffers

Do the Job

Check the tool that can be used for each job.

1. Han needs to sharpen the blades on his pruning shears before he can trim bushes.

   _____ **a.** sander   _____ **b.** grinder

2. Lara joins the seams between sections of automobiles at the plant where she works.

   _____ **a.** welding torch   _____ **b.** power drill

3. Sam needs to cut through several layers of heavy fabric to make parts for clothing.

   _____ **a.** circular saw   _____ **b.** grinder

4. Marsha is applying paint to the handmade cabinets she sells in her store.

   _____ **a.** buffer   _____ **b.** paint sprayer

5. Eddy has to make holes in the top and sides of a desk before he can bolt the parts together.

   _____ **a.** power drill   _____ **b.** welding torch

6. Sergei is smoothing the surface of the new wood floor in a hotel meeting room.

   _____ **a.** vacuum cleaner   _____ **b.** sander

7. Anna will put a shine on the surface of the floor after Sergei is finished.

   _____ **a.** glue gun   _____ **b.** buffer

8. Franco cleans an office building. Every night he cleans the carpets in all the offices.

   _____ **a.** vacuum cleaner   _____ **b.** sander

9. Jill needs to put a sheet of plastic over a window opening in the house she is remodeling.

   _____ **a.** power drill   _____ **b.** staple gun

10. Sarah works on a machine assembly line.

    _____ **a.** power screwdriver   _____ **b.** circular saw

What Are the Dangers?

What are the safety risks in each picture? Write the letters of the risks on the line. Answers may be used more than once.

---

a. dust scratching the eyes
b. shoulder or wrist pain
c. hearing problems

d. back pain
e. difficulty breathing
f. deep cut or puncture wound

g. electrical shock

1.

_____

3.

_____

2.

_____

4.

_____

Be Safe

Look at the list of safety risks on page 30. How can workers avoid these risks? Write rules for safe use of power tools. Each rule may apply to one or more tools

Tool(s)   Rule for Safe Use

_____ : _____

_____ : _____

_____ : _____

_____ : _____

_____ : _____

_____ : _____

What about You?

Have you used any of the power tools on page 28? If so, which ones? Where did you use them? For what jobs did you use them? Fill in the chart. If you have used other power tools, include those on the chart.

Tool	Location	Job/Purpose

Heavy Machinery

Study and Learn

Here are heavy machines that you can see in different types of workplaces.

drill press

die press

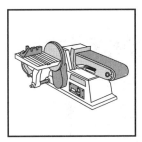
bench sander

table saw

trash compactor

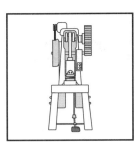
baler

sewing machine

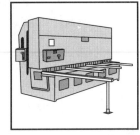
guillotine shears

tractor

mower

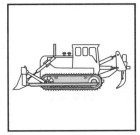
bulldozer

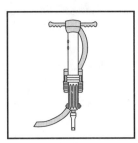
jackhammer

What Do They Use?

Write the name of the heavy machine that would be best for each worker or situation. Use the words on page 32.

1. A construction worker uses a _____ to move large amounts of earth or rocks.

2. A machine shop worker uses a _____ to punch holes in sheet metal.

3. A supermarket worker uses a _____ to crush garbage so it can be disposed of easily.

4. An office worker uses a _____ to pack empty cartons together for recycling.

5. A textile worker uses a _____ to put pieces of cloth together and make clothing.

6. A groundskeeper uses a _____ to keep grass short.

7. A farm worker uses a _____ to pull a plow or a harvester.

8. A factory worker uses a _____ to make metal or wood surfaces smooth.

9. A road worker uses a _____ to break up the road surface before making repairs on the road.

10. A worker in an envelope factory uses a _____ to cut thick piles of paper.

11. A metal worker uses a _____ to cut out specially shaped pieces from sheet metal.

What Is the Danger?

Write the best warning sign to go with each picture. Some pictures
may require more than one warning.

Wear Safety Glasses	No Loose Clothing	Use Ear Protection
Turn Off before Repair	Keep Hands Clear	Cover Long Hair

1.

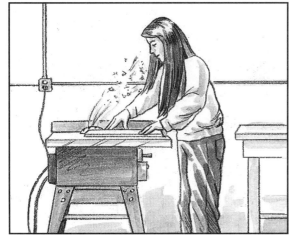

_____

3.

_____

2.

_____

4.

_____

Know the Risks

What long-term health problem can each worker get from the job?
Check the best answer.

1. A farm worker operates a tractor all day in the sun.
   _____ **a.** skin problems _____ **b.** stomach problems

2. A repair worker bends and kneels all day to fix broken machines.
   _____ **a.** lung problems _____ **b.** back injury

3. A textile worker cuts material that releases small fabric particles into
   the air.
   _____ **a.** foot injury _____ **b.** breathing disorder

4. A machine shop worker turns the controls on a drill press over and
   over again.
   _____ **a.** wrist injury _____ **b.** frequent headaches

5. A furniture maker uses a bench sander to smooth pieces of wood
   before using them.
   _____ **a.** skin problems _____ **b.** eye injury

What about You?

Think about the heavy machines in this lesson. Do you see any of
them at your workplace? If so, which ones? Who uses them?
What safety measures do those workers take to avoid risks?
Create a chart on separate paper.

Machine	Worker	Safety Measure

Operating Parts

Study and Learn

Here are common operating parts that are found on many tools and machines.

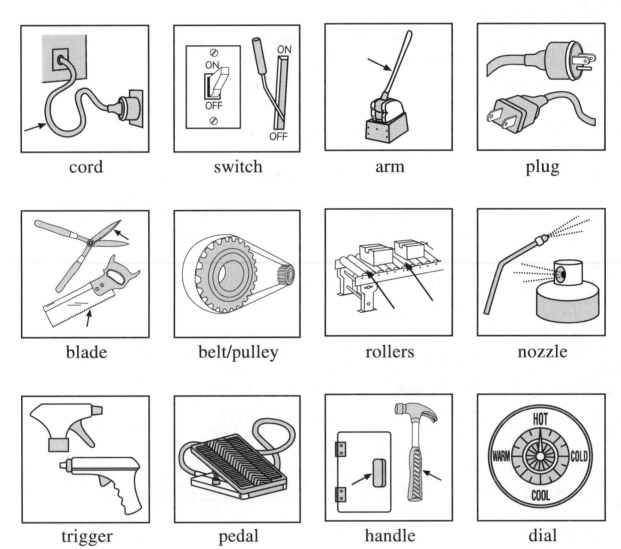

cord	switch	arm	plug
blade	belt/pulley	rollers	nozzle
trigger	pedal	handle	dial

What Does It Do?

Complete each sentence with the word for the correct operating part.
Use the words on page 36.

1. Val presses the _____ on her sewing machine to make it run.

2. Hong pulls the _____ on his paint gun when he wants paint to spray out.

3. Dave flips the _____ on his floor buffer to OFF before he unplugs the buffer.

4. Margo sets the _____ on the steam press to control the temperature.

5. Abdul regularly cleans the _____ of his glue gun so that the glue will flow out easily.

6. Silas uses a heavy-duty _____ to get electrical power to his industrial vacuum cleaner.

7. Jud keeps the _____ on his shears very sharp so that they will cut smoothly.

8. Sally pulls down the _____ on her die press to cut out pieces of metal.

9. Lan uses a _____ system to bring clothes from the back of the dry-cleaning store to the front.

10. Ray always carries his tools by their _____.

What Is the Danger?

Complete the warning for the worker in each picture. Be prepared to say what can happen if the worker does not follow the warning.

> Don't open that! It's still plugged in.
> Take off your bracelet near the belt and pulley.
> Don't turn that on! The cord is frayed.
> The rollers on that belt are loose.

1.

Careful. _____

3.

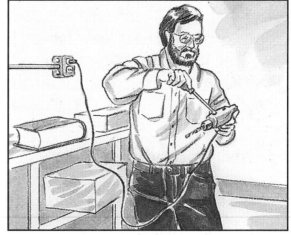

Watch it! _____

2.

Look out! _____

4.

Hold it! _____

Replace the Part

Here are common safety problems for operating parts. Write the correct word beneath its description.

frayed	dull	brittle	stuck

1. The cover on your vacuum cleaner's cord is tearing away in long pieces. You can see the electric wires inside it.

   The cord is _____.

2. The rubber belt on your factory sewing machine is old and dry. When the belt turns fast, parts of the rubber break away.

   The belt is _____ and ready to snap.

3. You pull the trigger on a paint gun to make the gun work. But you can't move the trigger back to OFF.

   The trigger is _____.

4. The blade on your table saw doesn't cut well anymore. You need to replace it with a sharp blade.

   The old blade is _____.

What about You?

Think about the tools and machines you use at work. What operating parts do they have? What do you do to take care of those parts? Create a chart on separate paper.

Tool	Parts	Care
hammer	handle	make sure handle is tightly attached

Safety Features

Study and Learn

Here are common safety guards used on different tools and machines in the workplace.

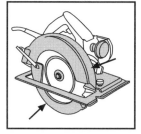
blade guard

pulley guard

lockout guard

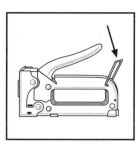
safety latch

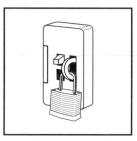
plate guard

cutoff switch

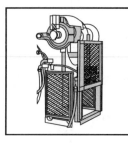
gate

body bar

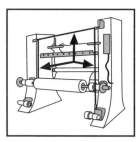
trip wire

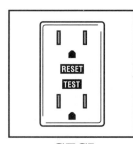
GFCI

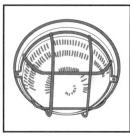
warning light

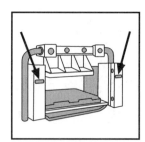
electric eye

What Does It Do?

Match each safety guard to what it does.

a. blade guard	**d.** warning light	**g.** GFCI
b. electric eye	**e.** lockout guard	**h.** trip wire
c. body bar	**f.** plate guard	**i.** gate

_____ **1.** stops a worker's body from falling into a machine

_____ **2.** blocks fingers and hands from machine parts that cut

_____ **3.** turns off a machine when a worker's body pushes against it

_____ **4.** stops plugs from sending electric shocks from wall outlets

_____ **5.** blocks a worker from entering an area where a machine is operating

_____ **6.** turns off a machine when an object crosses its beam

_____ **7.** stops workers from turning on a broken machine

_____ **8.** flashes when there is danger in the work area

_____ **9.** covers a switch so a machine cannot be turned on accidentally

Do the Job

Write the safety guards that do each job. Use the words on page 40.

1. These keep workers away from machine parts: _____

2. These stop workers from turning on a machine: _____

3. These turn a machine off if there is a problem: _____

What Do They Need?

Check the best safety guard for the worker in each situation.

1. Miguel is a carpenter. One day the belt on his bench sander breaks. Right away he needs to use a

   ___ **a.** cutoff switch   ___ **b.** warning light

2. Sophia is a fabric cutter. She pushes the fabric into guillotine shears. Her machine needs to have a

   ___ **a.** safety latch   ___ **b.** blade guard

3. George uses a jackhammer to repair streets. He does not want someone to start the jackhammer while he is on break. He uses a

   ___ **a.** safety latch   ___ **b.** body bar

4. Virgilio runs a drill press at a machine shop. One day the drill press breaks down. Until it is repaired, the shop needs to put on a

   ___ **a.** cutoff switch   ___ **b.** lockout guard

5. Jan works an overhead crane that carries heavy parts in an auto assembly plant. To make sure no one turns off the crane while it is moving, he covers the switch with a

   ___ **a.** trip wire   ___ **b.** plate guard

6. Mike runs a trash compactor. Large belts raise and lower the compactor. To make sure nothing gets caught in the belts, the compactor has a

   ___ **a.** pulley guard   ___ **b.** cutoff switch

7. Armando is a machine operator in a processing plant. When he turns on the machines, he has to make sure no one comes near them. His area needs to have a

   ___ **a.** gate   ___ **b.** safety latch

Be Safe

Read each safety rule. Check **Always** or **Never** to make each rule true.

Always Never

_____ _____ 1. A safety guard should let a worker touch the moving parts of a machine.

_____ _____ 2. A safety guard should be easy to remove if a worker doesn't want to use it.

_____ _____ 3. A safety guard should prevent objects from falling into the moving parts of a machine.

_____ _____ 4. A safety guard should permit comfortable and easy operation of a machine.

_____ _____ 5. A safety guard should block the worker's view of what the machine is doing.

_____ _____ 6. Lockout guards and plate guards should be small and easy to pull off.

What about You?

Do you see safety guards on tools and machines at your workplace?
If so, name them in the chart below. Then give a reason why the guards are important.

Tool/Machine	Guard	Reason
guillotine shears	blade guard	to prevent cutting off fingers
garden shears	safety latch	so shears will not open accidentally

Unit 2 Review

For each tool, check the appropriate operating part and safety guard.
Make sure both items are on the tool.

1. bench sander
   - _____ **a.** belt and cutoff switch
   - _____ **b.** trigger and blade guard

2. sewing machine
   - _____ **a.** pedal and cutoff switch
   - _____ **b.** roller and trip wire

3. paint sprayer
   - _____ **a.** handle and warning light
   - _____ **b.** nozzle and safety latch

4. circular saw
   - _____ **a.** plug and blade guard
   - _____ **b.** arm and cutoff switch

5. glue gun
   - _____ **a.** trigger and safety latch
   - _____ **b.** dial and pulley guard

6. guillotine shears
   - _____ **a.** pulley and body bar
   - _____ **b.** blade and blade guard

7. power drill
   - _____ **a.** switch and plate guard
   - _____ **b.** cord and safety latch

8. wire cutters
   - _____ **a.** blade and safety latch
   - _____ **b.** handle and warning light

Write the hand tools, power tools, and heavy machines that have the same function.

9. Tools that cut wood: _____

10. Tools that cut fabric: _____

11. Tools that make surfaces or edges smooth: _____

12. Tools that cut metal: _____

13. Tools that break cement or rock: _____

UNIT 3
Health and Ergonomics

The conditions in which you work, the ways you move to perform your job, and the ways you use machines and other equipment affect your comfort and health. The study of these things is called ergonomics.

In Unit 3, you will learn about
- common work conditions that can affect health—noise, temperature, lighting, and others
- equipment for climbing and for lifting or moving things in the workplace
- movements common to many jobs and the ways to move safely

You will also learn about ways to reduce health and safety risks.

The conditions in which you work and the way you carry out your job are important to your long-term health. As you study these lessons, think about your own workplace and the conditions that can affect your health. Think about how you can use the language and information in these lessons to protect your health and feel better at work.

LESSON 10 — A Healthy Workplace

Study and Learn

Here are conditions in the workplace that can cause health problems.

eyestrain	weak lighting	confined space	loud noise
contaminated air	poor ventilation	temperature extremes	standing for long periods
wrong chair for the job	poor workstation design	cramped work position	repetitive motion

Be Safe

Check the work condition that can cause a health problem for each worker.

1. Van repairs large freezers. Sometimes he must bend his body to fit into a small space where a repair is needed.

   _____ **a.** repetitive motion   _____ **b.** cramped work position

2. Eva packs toys for shipment to stores. She works in a small room with no air conditioning and just one window.

   _____ **a.** loud noise   _____ **b.** poor ventilation

3. Minh operates a steam press in a laundry. All day long he pulls the control that lowers the press.

   _____ **a.** repetitive motion   _____ **b.** contaminated air

4. Janusz does construction work. He crawls inside large ground pipes to seal connections between the pipes.

   _____ **a.** confined space   _____ **b.** loud noise

5. In an auto assembly plant, Pat operates the spray gun that applies a chemical finish to the car seats.

   _____ **a.** wrong chair for job   _____ **b.** contaminated air

6. Micheline is a security guard at a shopping mall. All day she walks from one end of the mall to the other.

   _____ **a.** standing for long periods   _____ **b.** weak lighting

7. Brahima lays wires for a television cable company. He works outside all year.

   _____ **a.** temperature extremes   _____ **b.** poor workstation design

8. Angelina is a garment worker. When she sits at her sewing machine, her feet do not touch the ground. She has to stretch to reach the pedals of the sewing machine.

   _____ **a.** poor ventilation   _____ **b.** wrong chair for the job

9. Ray is a pressman in a printing plant. The presses that he works around are very noisy.

   _____ **a.** repetitive motion   _____ **b.** loud noise

What Is the Problem?

In each picture, identify one or more work conditions that can cause health problems. Use the conditions on page 46.

1.

_____

_____

3.

_____

_____

2.

_____

_____

4.

_____

_____

Health Problems

Look again at the pictures on page 48. Write the letters of the health risks for each worker. Some pictures have more than one health risk. You may use answers more than once.

a. back pain	**d.** leg cramps	**g.** wrist injury
b. hearing problems	**e.** eyestrain	**h.** neck pain
c. heat stress	**f.** pain in arms	**i.** headache

Picture 1: _____   Picture 3: _____

Picture 2: _____   Picture 4: _____

What about You?

Think about the conditions at your workplace. In the chart, write *OK* if you are satisfied with the condition. Write *Not OK* if you think a change is needed. If change is needed, write your idea of how to improve the condition.

Condition	OK/Not OK	Idea for Improvement
ventilation		
air quality		
lighting		
temperature		
workstation design		
seating (chairs/benches)		
noise level		

Moving Things Around

Study and Learn

Here are common devices that help workers lift or move things in the workplace.

hand truck

dolly

cart

wheelbarrow

forklift

front-end loader

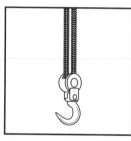
hook

platform

ramps

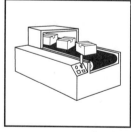
conveyor belt

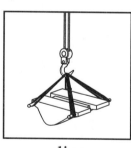
sling

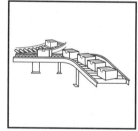
roller belt

Do the Job

Check the best device for each worker to use.

1. A mover is taking a washing machine into a home.
   _____ **a.** hand truck   _____ **b.** roller belt

2. An auto repair worker is lifting an engine out of a car.
   _____ **a.** wheelbarrow   _____ **b.** hook

3. A warehouse worker is moving boxes to the shelves.
   _____ **a.** sling   _____ **b.** hand truck

4. A waiter is taking dirty plates to the kitchen.
   _____ **a.** cart   _____ **b.** ramp

5. A gardener is moving dirt away from a work area.
   _____ **a.** dolly   _____ **b.** wheelbarrow

6. A construction worker is pushing large piles of dirt back from an excavation.
   _____ **a.** front-end loader   _____ **b.** hand truck

7. A food delivery worker is unloading boxes of frozen meat from the street down to the basement of a restaurant.
   _____ **a.** roller belt   _____ **b.** wheelbarrow

8. A hospital aide is moving a patient in a wheelchair down to an X-ray room on a lower part of the same floor.
   _____ **a.** ramp   _____ **b.** conveyor belt

9. A worker in a meat-packing plant is taking packed crates to the shipping department.
   _____ **a.** wheelbarrow   _____ **b.** forklift

10. The salesperson at a home improvement store has to get products off high storage shelves for customers.
    _____ **a.** platform   _____ **b.** conveyor belt

What Do They Need?

Write the device or devices that can help each worker do the job safely. Some choices may be used more than once.

platform	hand truck	forklift	wheelbarrow
conveyor belt	dolly	sling	ramp

1.

3.

2.

4.

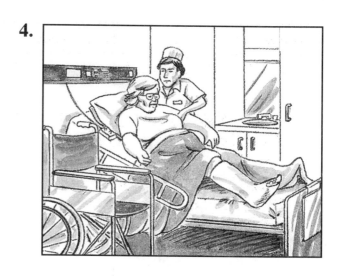

What's the Risk?

Look again at the pictures on page 52. Write the letter of the safety risks for each worker. You may use answers more than once.

---

a. back injury from lifting or carrying heavy items
b. foot or leg injury from falling materials
c. shoulder or neck injury from reaching to do a job
d. body injury from slipping or falling
e. hand injury from materials hitting together

Picture 1: _____   Picture 3: _____

Picture 2: _____   Picture 4: _____

What about You?

Which devices for moving things do you see where you work? Where in the workplace are they located? Who uses them? Fill in the chart. If your workplace has devices that are not in the lesson, include them too.

Device	Location(s)	Used by
ramp	entrance	delivery people, customers in wheelchairs
hand truck	kept in mailroom	mail clerks

Safe Movement in the Workplace

Study and Learn

Here are words for common movements that people make in the workplace.

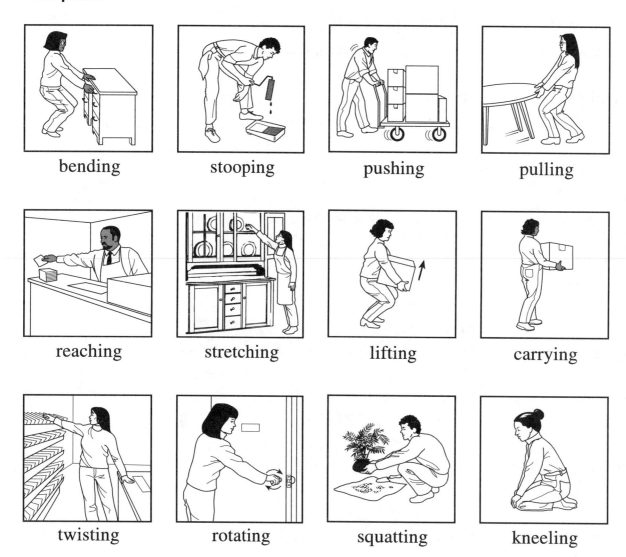

bending	stooping	pushing	pulling
reaching	stretching	lifting	carrying
twisting	rotating	squatting	kneeling

Repeated Movements

Some job injuries happen because workers repeat the same movements over long periods of time. Check the body part that can be hurt most by repeated movements in each job.

1. An assembly line worker lifts boxes from the floor to a conveyor belt.
   _____ a. feet   _____ b. back

2. A repair worker reaches across the work table for tools.
   _____ a. fingers   _____ b. shoulders

3. A plumber squats to fix pipes under a sink.
   _____ a. knees   _____ b. arms

4. A housekeeper stoops to clean under furniture.
   _____ a. wrists   _____ b. back

5. A stock clerk twists his body to move packages from the floor to the shelves.
   _____ a. waist/hips _____ b. shoulders

6. A sales clerk stretches to take items down from shelves.
   _____ a. chest   _____ b. shoulders

7. A furniture builder rotates a screwdriver to tighten screws in wood.
   _____ a. eyes   _____ b. wrist

8. A flooring installer kneels for long periods to lay tile or linoleum.
   _____ a. knees   _____ b. eyes

9. A warehouse worker pushes or pulls a hand truck loaded with heavy cartons.
   _____ a. back   _____ b. feet

10. A supermarket worker bends to stock products on low shelves.
    _____ a. elbow   _____ b. back

Move Safely!

What can each worker do to reduce the pain he or she feels from the job? Check the right answer.

1. Serge lifts heavy boxes onto hand trucks all day. His back always hurts at the end of the day. He should
   _____ **a.** bend his knees when he lifts
   _____ **b.** keep his knees straight and bend over when he lifts

2. Lou kneels to clean floors all day. His knees always hurt at the end of the day. He should
   _____ **a.** squat and not kneel to do his job
   _____ **b.** wear knee pads or put down a pad where he kneels

3. Phu bends over a table to assemble computer boards. His back always hurts at the end of the day. He should
   _____ **a.** hold the computer boards in his hands while he works
   _____ **b.** lower the height of his chair or find a shorter one

4. Athina stretches all day to get parts off a conveyor belt. Her neck and shoulders always hurt. She should
   _____ **a.** stand on a small platform or stool to get things
   _____ **b.** wear shoes with taller heels to gain more height

5. Phil pulls carts with heavy loads behind him. His back and shoulders hurt at the end of the day. He should
   _____ **a.** push the carts in front of him
   _____ **b.** take lighter loads and make more trips

6. Maurice carries heavy bags by balancing them on his hip. His back and hips hurt at the end of the day. He should
   _____ **a.** hold them over his head while he carries them
   _____ **b.** hold them in front with both arms or use a dolly

Lifting and Carrying

Read each statement. Write **Y** for **Yes** if you think it gives good advice. Write **N** for **No** if you think it gives bad advice. Be ready to explain your answers.

_____ **1.** Bend at the waist to pick up something heavy.

_____ **2.** When you carry a heavy box, hold it to one side and support it with your hip.

_____ **3.** When possible, lift things at the same level as your arms, not where you must stoop or stretch.

_____ **4.** Ask for help if something is too heavy to lift.

_____ **5.** Look to see that the floor ahead is clear before you carry things.

_____ **6.** Hold things away from your body to carry them.

_____ **7.** Turn your whole body if you need to lift something and move it in a different direction.

_____ **8.** Pile things high in your arms if you have a lot to carry, so you don't have to make as many trips.

What about You?

Look back at the words on page 54. Which body movements do you make at work? Do you ever feel pain from these movements? If so, from which ones? Where in your body do you feel the pain? Create a chart on separate paper. Discuss what you can do to reduce or prevent the pain.

Movement	Pain/No Pain	Part(s) of Body

Climbing in the Workplace

Study and Learn

Here are common devices for climbing or working above the ground.

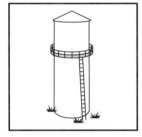

fixed ladder

stepladder

rolling ladder

straight ladder

extension ladder

hook ladder

scaffold

platform ladder

side rail(1)/
cross brace(2)

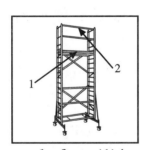

platform(1)/
guardrail(2)

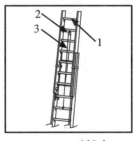

rungs(1)/
pulley(2)/rope(3)

steps/
handrails

What to Use

Check the climbing device that each worker can use to do the job safely.

1. Severin is installing gutters on a two-story house.
   _____ **a.** rolling ladder   _____ **b.** extension ladder

2. Hoa is changing the wiring for a kitchen ceiling light.
   _____ **a.** stepladder   _____ **b.** extension ladder

3. Joel and Omar are painting the top part of a wall in a train station.
   _____ **a.** scaffold   _____ **b.** platform ladder

4. Habib is checking a leak in the roof of a water tower that is 200 feet tall.
   _____ **a.** stepladder   _____ **b.** fixed ladder

5. Mahmoud is taking down several books from different sections of a high shelf in his bookstore.
   _____ **a.** rolling ladder   _____ **b.** fixed ladder

6. Manny and Albert are installing windows on the fifth floor of an apartment building.
   _____ **a.** extension ladder   _____ **b.** scaffold

7. Anita is restocking boxes on high storage shelves in a department store stockroom.
   _____ **a.** straight ladder   _____ **b.** rolling ladder

8. Lenny is replacing a first-floor window.
   _____ **a.** stepladder   _____ **b.** straight ladder

9. Katya is checking the roof of a house to see if any shingles need to be replaced.
   _____ **a.** fixed ladder   _____ **b.** extension ladder

Do's and Don'ts: Ladders

Study these safety rules for using ladders. Write the numbers of the rules that each worker should follow. Discuss what can happen if the rules are not followed.

1. Keep body within side rails.
2. Set base on a level surface.
3. Hold on with at least one hand.
4. Never let two workers climb on a single ladder.
5. Lock the cross brace.
6. Never stand on the top step.
7. Check that all rungs are in good condition.
8. Keep ladder away from wiring.
9. Wear shoes with nonslip soles.

2.

1.

3.

Safety Tips

Complete each sentence with the correct word.

| rope | handrail | rungs | steps | guardrails |

1. Make sure the _____ of a rolling ladder are dry. You can

   slip if there is any water on them.

2. Hold onto the _____ for greater security when you go

   up or down a rolling ladder.

3. Keep the _____ on an extension ladder in good

   condition. If it is frayed and breaks, the ladder can fall.

4. Make sure the _____ on your ladder are strong and in

   good condition before you climb the ladder.

5. Make sure the _____ around any scaffold or platform

   are high and strong, to prevent a fall.

What about You?

Look again at the climbing devices on page 58. Do you see any of
them in your workplace? If so, which ones? Where are they used?
What jobs do they help workers do? Create a chart on separate paper.

Device	Location	Job(s)

Unit 3 Review

Write the letter of the term described in each situation.

a. stepladder	**e.** hearing loss	**h.** temperature extremes
b. cart	**f.** conveyor belt	**i.** contaminated air
c. rungs	**g.** wheelbarrow	**j.** poor ventilation
d. guardrail		

_____ 1. Ha's workplace fills with fumes when chemicals leak from old storage tanks. He worries about this safety problem.

_____ 2. Carmilla stands near the edge of a high scaffold to paint. Without this protection she can fall.

_____ 3. Aaron stands on his toes and stretches his arms to put cartons on a high shelf. This device will help.

_____ 4. Tai's workshop has small windows and no fans to move air. This condition can cause health problems.

_____ 5. Van needs to move boxes from one side of a factory floor to the other. This device will help.

_____ 6. Richard uses a ladder in his job. Before he climbs on it, he should always check these.

_____ 7. Tony's work area is always full of noise from power drills. He worries about this problem.

_____ 8. Blanca wants to remove a pile of bricks from a construction area. This will make the job easier.

_____ 9. Stefan mows lawns in the summer and operates a snowplow in the winter. He worries about health problems caused by this.

_____ 10. Loni is a nurse's aide. She uses this to take medical equipment and medications to patients' rooms.

UNIT 4

Safety Information and Labeling

Tags on machinery and labels on containers give important safety information. The tags give warnings such as when it is dangerous to turn a machine on. The labels give information about safe use of the products, possible health risks, first aid in case of an accident, and storing or disposing of a product safely.

The lessons in this unit will help you understand tags and labels so that you can use the information that they provide. You will learn
  • how to recognize situations in which safety warnings apply
  • what equipment to use to protect yourself
  • what to do in case of an accident with a product at work
  • how to recognize common warning symbols on tags and labels

As you study these lessons, think about the machines at your workplace and the products that you or your co-workers use. You may not use those machines or products yourself. But you can be exposed to risks if others are using them. The warnings and instructions on tags and labels are vital to your safety and the safety of workers around you.

LESSON 14 Labels and Tags

Study and Learn

Here are common warning labels and tags that you can see on tools and machines in the workplace:

Do Not Start
Equipment

Lockout:
Do Not Operate

Do Not
Open Valve

Shut Off
before Servicing

Radiation
Hazard

Keep Guards
in Place

Keep Hands
Away

Objects May Be
Thrown from
Machine

Pinch Point

High Voltage

Hot Surface

Rotating Blades

What Is the Danger?

Check the tag or label that is most important for each worker.

1. Enrique is mowing the grounds around a school. There are sticks and rocks in the area he is cutting.
    _____ **a.** Do Not Start Equipment _____ **b.** Objects May Be Thrown from Machine

2. Francesca operates an X-ray machine in a dentist's office.
    _____ **a.** Keep Hands Away _____ **b.** Radiation Hazard

3. Subra works for a catering business. The ovens in the kitchen run all day.
    _____ **a.** Hot Surface _____ **b.** High Voltage

4. Al cuts wood with a table saw. A hard piece of plastic around the blade stops it from cutting off his fingers.
    _____ **a.** Do Not Start Equipment _____ **b.** Keep Guards in Place

5. Tam is repairing a broken water heater. Hot water can burn him if it flows while he is working.
    _____ **a.** Do Not Open Valve _____ **b.** Keep Hands Away

6. Sara is starting her shift. During the last shift one of the machines broke down and has not been fixed yet.
    _____ **a.** Keep Guards in Place _____ **b.** Lockout: Do Not Operate

What Does It Say?

Write the tags or labels from page 64 that give these warnings.

1. Watch out for danger to your body! _____

2. Use the safety features on the equipment! _____

3. Don't use this equipment! _____

What's the Warning?

Write the tag or label warnings that are most likely to appear on each tool or machine. You may use warnings more than once.

Rotating Blades	Pinch Point	Keep Guards in Place
Hot Surface	Keep Hands Away	Shut Off before Servicing
Objects May Be Thrown from Machine		

1.

_____

2.

_____

3.

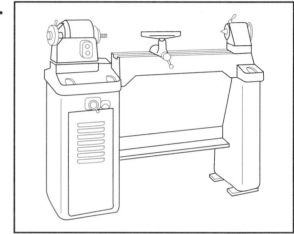

_____

4.

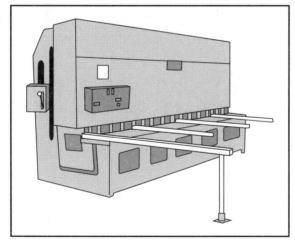

_____

Tags to Know

Some tags describe qualities that affect tool or machine safety. Write
the letter of the tag next to its meaning.

a. Starts Automatically	**c.** _____ Volts **e.** Fragile Parts
b. Defective Machinery	**d.** Inspected by _____ on _____

_____ **1.** This is the type of electric power that safely runs a tool or
machine.

_____ **2.** The machine parts can break easily.

_____ **3.** This tool or machine was poorly made or has bad parts.

_____ **4.** This machine was checked for safety.

_____ **5.** This machine is programmed to start and stop on its own.

What about You?

What tags or labels with warnings do you see at your workplace?
On which tools or machines do they appear? Why are they there?

Tag/Label	Tool/Machine	Reason

Warnings on Labels

Study and Learn

These labels warn of possible dangers and health hazards from workplace materials.

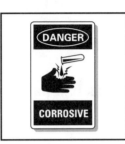

Toxic

Corrosive

Irritant

Carcinogen

Flammable/
Combustible

For External
Use Only

Harmful
if Ingested

Contents
under Pressure

Respiratory
Hazard

Do Not Inhale
Vapors or Fumes

Use in Well
Ventilated Area

Avoid Prolonged
Exposure

Be Safe

Check the answer that best completes each statement.

1. The label says "For External Use Only." You should not
   _____ **a.** use this product inside the house
   _____ **b.** eat or drink this product

2. The label says "Toxic." The product
   _____ **a.** can make you sick or kill you if you swallow it
   _____ **b.** will catch on fire easily

3. The label says "Irritant." The product
   _____ **a.** is corrosive and will eat through metal
   _____ **b.** will cause a rash or itching on your skin

4. The label says "Use in Well Ventilated Area." The product is probably
   _____ **a.** dangerous to use in a small, closed room
   _____ **b.** dangerous to use outside in the backyard

5. The label says "Contents under Pressure." The can that holds the product may
   _____ **a.** burst or explode if exposed to heat
   _____ **b.** burn you if you pick it up without gloves

6. The label says "Avoid Prolonged Exposure." The product
   _____ **a.** can harm you if you use it for a long time
   _____ **b.** can harm you right away

7. The label says "Carcinogen." The product
   _____ **a.** can catch on fire easily
   _____ **b.** can cause cancer over a long period of use

8. The label says "Harmful if Ingested." You should not
   _____ **a.** use this product near fire
   _____ **b.** use this product on or near food

Safety Warnings

Check the label that best warns each worker about a possible health hazard in his or her job.

1. A gardener spreads fertilizing chemicals with his bare hands. He then goes inside to have lunch.

    _____ **a.** Corrosive   _____ **b.** Harmful if Ingested

2. A cabinetmaker uses a strong polish to put the finish on a cabinet. She works in a small room with no windows.

    _____ **a.** Use in Well Ventilated Area   _____ **b.** Carcinogen

3. A restaurant worker uses oven cleaner to remove hardened food on the inside surface of the oven.

    _____ **a.** Flammable   _____ **b.** Avoid Prolonged Exposure

4. A laundry worker uses liquid bleach to take stains out of shirts and sweaters.

    _____ **a.** Contents under Pressure   _____ **b.** Toxic

5. A mechanic fixes leaks in refrigerators. He replaces the coolant with gas from cylinders.

    _____ **a.** For External Use Only   _____ **b.** Contents under Pressure

6. An auto shop worker sprays paint on car bodies. He breathes the vapors from the paint all day long.

    _____ **a.** Do Not Inhale Vapors or Fumes   _____ **b.** Harmful if Ingested

7. A janitor is putting trash in the incinerator. There are several spray cans in the trash.

    _____ **a.** Toxic   _____ **b.** Contents under Pressure

8. A hairdresser is coloring a customer's hair. He usually wears latex gloves to apply the color.

    _____ **a.** Irritant   _____ **b.** Corrosive

Labels and Protective Equipment

Match each warning label with the equipment that will best protect
the body from the health hazard. Some equipment can be used more
than once.

_____ 1. Avoid Contact with Eyes   **a.** gloves

_____ 2. Do Not Inhale Vapors   **b.** dust mask

_____ 3. Avoid Contact with Clothes   **c.** goggles

_____ 4. Skin Irritant   **d.** respirator

_____ 5. Do Not Inhale Particles   **e.** apron

_____ 6. Respiratory Hazard

_____ 7. Corrosive

Safety for You

**Do you use or see in your workplace products with warning labels
from this lesson?** What are the products? Which warning labels do
you see on them? What health hazards do they warn against? Fill
in the chart. Discuss what a worker has to do to use those products
safely.

Product	Warning Label	Health Hazard(s)

First Aid Information on Labels

Study and Learn

These first aid instructions appear on many products that are used in the workplace.

Rinse immediately

Flush with water

Flush eyes immediately

Wash with soap and water

Move to fresh air

Induce vomiting

Do not induce vomiting

Call Poison Control Center

Remove contaminated clothes

Give artificial respiration

Seek medical attention

See doctor if condition persists

What Should They Do?

Check the best first aid instruction for each worker to follow.

1. Mario accidentally swallows a small amount of liquid bleach that got into his coffee cup.
   _____ **a.** Give artificial respiration _____ **b.** Call Poison Control Center

2. Therese is using a strong cleanser to wash floors. Some of the liquid splashes into her eyes and irritates them.
   _____ **a.** Flush with water _____ **b.** Wash with soap and water

3. Kim is applying dry cleaning fluid to clothes in the back room of a laundry. She feels sickened by the fumes.
   _____ **a.** Move to fresh air _____ **b.** Call Poison Control Center

4. Carlos rebuilds car batteries. Acid from a battery spills onto his shirt and begins to corrode the fabric.
   _____ **a.** Remove contaminated clothing _____ **b.** Seek medical attention

5. Hanna spreads weed-killer on the lawns that she tends. One day the wind blows some of it into her eyes. After 24 hours her eyes are still red and painful.
   _____ **a.** Move to fresh air _____ **b.** See doctor if condition persists

6. Ahmed is polishing furniture. The polish is getting on his hands and causing a mild irritation.
   _____ **a.** Move to fresh air _____ **b.** Wash with soap and water

7. Ray is cleaning his computer screen. He accidentally sprays some of the cleaner in his eyes.
   _____ **a.** Wash with soap and water _____ **b.** Flush eyes immediately

8. Angelo is cleaning the carpets in a customer's home. The customer's little boy drinks a little bit of the carpet cleaning fluid.
   _____ **a.** Do not induce vomiting _____ **b.** Give artificial respiration

Read the Label

Complete the label with the correct word or phrase.

persists	artificial respiration	flush	fresh air
wash	Poison Control Center	induce vomiting	

FIRST AID TREATMENT

IF SWALLOWED: Do not _____. Call

_____ immediately.
2

IF IN EYES: _____ with plenty of water
3

for at least 15 minutes.

IF ON SKIN: _____ promptly with
4

soap and water. If irritation _____, seek
5

medical attention.

IF INHALED: Move victim to _____.
6

If breathing has stopped, apply _____.
7

Safety Checkup

Look again at the first aid instructions on page 74. Review your answers with a partner or group. Use the instructions and write **T** for **True** or **F** for **False** for each statement.

_____ 1. Consult a physician immediately if this product gets on your skin.

_____ 2. Lie down in a quiet room in the workplace if you get sick from breathing this product.

_____ 3. If this product gets in your eyes, wash them out with a lot of water for more than 15 minutes.

_____ 4. If you swallow this product, make yourself vomit.

_____ 5. If you stop breathing, a co-worker who knows how to do artificial respiration should try to help you.

_____ 6. If you get this product on your hands, use soap and water to wash it off.

Safety for You

Look at the label on one of the products you use or see in your workplace. What first aid instructions are there? Write them on the chart below. Discuss how a worker can use the product safely.

Product	First Aid Instructions

Safe Storage and Disposal

Study and Learn

These signs and instructions tell how to store and dispose of many products safely.

Do Not Discard in Trash

Do Not Puncture Container

Do Not Incinerate

Infectious Waste

Store at Room Temperature

Do Not Store near Food

Store away from Heat or Flame

Do Not Store below 32°F

Replace Cap after Each Use

Keep Container Tightly Closed

Flush Spills with Water

Chemical Storage Area

What Is the Warning?

Check the instruction that tells a worker how to avoid each hazard.

1. This product is combustible.
   _____ **a.** Do Not Store below 32°F   _____ **b.** Store away from Heat or Flame

2. This product makes people sick if they eat it.
   _____ **a.** Do Not Store near Food   _____ **b.** Do Not Discard in Trash

3. The fumes from this product can make people sick.
   _____ **a.** Keep Container Tightly Closed _____ **b.** Store at Room Temperature

4. Workers must be careful not to spill this product.
   _____ **a.** Infectious Waste   _____ **b.** Replace Cap after Each Use

5. The pressure in this container can make it explode.
   _____ **a.** Keep Container Tightly Closed _____ **b.** Do Not Puncture Container

6. The contents of this container can cause diseases.
   _____ **a.** Infectious Waste   _____ **b.** Replace Cap after Each Use

7. You must not freeze this product.
   _____ **a.** Do Not Incinerate   _____ **b.** Do Not Store below 32°F

8. Workers must use a lot of water to clean up this product if it gets on the floor.
   _____ **a.** Flush Spills with Water   _____ **b.** Infectious Waste

9. This product must not get very hot or very cold.
   _____ **a.** Do Not Store near Food   _____ **b.** Store at Room Temperature

10. This product will explode if you put it in a fire.
    _____ **a.** Do Not Discard in Trash   _____ **b.** Do Not Incinerate

Follow Instructions

Write the storage or disposal instruction that each worker should follow. Discuss why the instruction is important.

Do Not Store near Food	Keep Container Tightly Closed
Do Not Discard in Trash	Do Not Incinerate

1.

_____

3.

_____

2.

_____

4.

_____

Be Safe

Check the answer that explains how to follow the instructions.

1. The label says "Do Not Store below 32°F."
   _____ **a.** Keep the product in a freezer.
   _____ **b.** Keep the product in a cabinet.

2. The label says "Flush Spills with Water."
   _____ **a.** Use wet towels to wipe up the spill.
   _____ **b.** Use a hose to wash away the spill.

3. The label says "Do Not Discard in Trash."
   _____ **a.** Find out how your company disposes of containers like this.
   _____ **b.** Wrap the container in a plastic bag before you put it in the trash.

4. The label on a cabinet says "Chemical Storage Area."
   _____ **a.** Open the cabinet only to remove or store chemicals you need for your job.
   _____ **b.** Put all chemical containers on one shelf so you can put your lunch in the same cabinet.

Safety for You

Look at products you use or see in your workplace. Where are they stored? Where are they disposed of? Do those procedures match the instructions on the product labels? Create a chart on separate paper.

Product	Storage	Disposal	OK/Not OK

Unit 4 Review

For each type of hazard, write a warning, a first aid instruction, and a storage or disposal instruction that go together.

1. Breathing

Warning _____

First Aid _____

Storage/Disposal _____

2. Skin/Eyes

Warning _____

First Aid _____

Storage/Disposal _____

3. Fire/Explosion

Warning _____

First Aid _____

Storage/Disposal _____

4. Poison

Warning _____

First Aid _____

Storage/Disposal _____

Safety Tool Kit

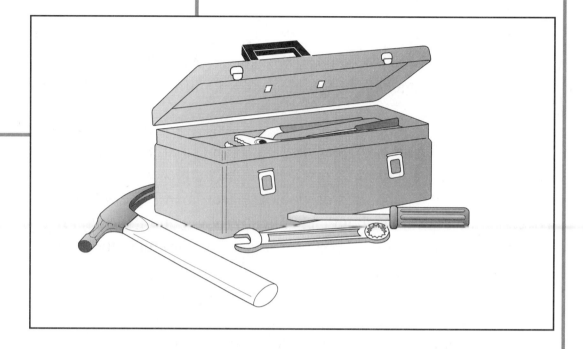

The information and activities in this Safety Tool Kit focus on specific topics to help you work more safely.

"Reading an MSDS" will help you understand Material Safety Data Sheets. These sheets give important information about chemical products used in many workplaces.

"Glossary of Health and Injury Terms" gives common terms and simple explanations for many health problems. You may need to discuss a problem with a co-worker, supervisor, or health-care worker.

"Health and Safety Policies" introduces policies dealing with workplace safety. Many companies have policies like these.

"Lockouts and Tagouts (LOTO)" identifies very important warnings used with heavy machinery. Following proper LOTO procedures can be a matter of life and death.

Do you ever feel pain at work or after work? The simple exercises in the last Tool Kit section can help reduce or prevent some of the pain.

Reading an MSDS

MSDS stands for "Material Safety Data Sheet." An MSDS gives details about chemical products used for cleaning, manufacturing, repair, and many other jobs.

The information on an MSDS is very important in all jobs where chemical products are used. A product can be dangerous if a worker does not understand what it is or what its hazards are. The MSDS answers many questions about a chemical product and its safety. It gives more information than you will find on the product label. The information tells you

- what the chemical is and how it can be dangerous
- what clothing or equipment to wear for protection
- how to avoid fires, explosions, and other accidents
- what to do for first aid if you are exposed to the chemical
- what to do if there is a fire, spill, or other accident

Sometimes you see numbers on an MSDS. These numbers show the risk levels in using the material. Zero (0) means no risk. One (1) means low risk. Two (2) and three (3) mean higher risk. Four (4) stands for the most serious risk.

The law requires all companies that use chemical products to make MSDS information available to employees. Employees have a right to know about the possible hazards of a chemical they use on the job. Find out where your company keeps MSDS files. If you are worried about a chemical at your workplace, look at the MSDS. If you do not understand all the information, ask someone to help you read it. The information can be very important for your safety.

Summary of an MSDS

Here is a short summary of an MSDS. It describes the general areas of information you will find on an MSDS. A real MSDS will be longer. But you don't have to read all of an MSDS if you have a question. Usually, one or two sections will give the answer you need.

1. **Chemical Product and Company Identification**
   - gives name of product and explains how it is used
   - gives name and address of company that makes the product

2. **Information on Ingredients**
   - lists hazardous and nonhazardous chemicals in the product
   - identifies limits of safe exposure to the product

3. **Hazards Identification**
   - gives hazard ratings (0–4) for the product
   - lists possible hazards to parts of the body
   - identifies any cancer risk from the product

4. **First Aid Measures**
   - gives medical information and information about first aid treatment for employees who are exposed to the product

5. **Fire-Fighting Measures**
   - lists combustible chemicals in the product
   - tells how to avoid fire risks when using the product
   - tells how to put out a fire that starts from the product and what protective equipment to wear

6. **Accidental Release Measures**
   - tells how to clean up the product when it leaks or spills
   - lists protective equipment to wear during cleanup

7. **Handling and Storage**
   - gives information for safe handling and storage of the product

8. Exposure Controls/Personal Protection
- tells companies how to lower health risks for employees who are exposed to the product
- lists personal protective equipment employees can wear when using the product

9. Physical and Chemical Properties
- tells how the product will behave at different temperatures
- tells how the product will behave when mixed with water

10. Stability and Reactivity
- lists other chemicals that can cause a hazard if they are mixed with the product
- lists materials that can create a hazard if they come into contact with the product

11. Toxicological Information
- gives information about whether the product is toxic, including health effects on both humans and animals

12. Ecological Information
- tells how a spill of the product can be hazardous to animal life and pollute rivers, land areas, air, etc.

13. Disposal Considerations
- gives information for proper disposal of the product

14. Transport Information
- tells how to pack and label the product for safe transport and shipping

Using an MSDS

Check the section of the MSDS where each worker can find information or help.

1. Vang works in a factory that makes batteries. She wants to know more about possible cancer risk from exposure to the liquid metal used in making the product.

   _____ **a.** Fire-Fighting Measures   _____ **b.** Hazards Identification

2. Ben's plumbing company uses copper pipes. The copper dust irritates his eyes when he cuts the pipes. He wants to know how he can protect his eyes while he works.

   _____ **a.** Exposure Controls/   _____ **b.** Handling and Storage
   Personal Protection

3. Manny works in a perfume factory that uses a special alcohol. He wants to know how long he can breathe the vapors before there is a possible health risk.

   _____ **a.** Transport Information   _____ **b.** Information on Ingredients

4. Jim is an employee at a plastics factory. He hears other workers say that a chemical they use is highly flammable. He wants to know if this is true.

   _____ **a.** Disposal Considerations   _____ **b.** Fire-Fighting Measures

5. Olga works for a printing company. Some of the ink spills on her hands and irritates them. She wants to know the best way to remove the ink from her skin.

   _____ **a.** First Aid Measures   _____ **b.** Accidental Release Measures

6. Irena works in a factory that uses a particular chemical to make weed killer. She wants to know more about what this chemical is and how it is used.

   _____ **a.** Chemical Product and   _____ **b.** First Aid Measures
   Company Information

Glossary of Health and Injury Terms

This glossary explains common words to describe injuries, pain, and other health problems that develop from workplace conditions. It is important to use accurate words when you explain a problem you are having to a doctor.

Note: This glossary gives only the most common use of each word. It does not list all uses for every word.

ache: to have a dull pain that continues for several hours or days

- *Betty's arms still ache from the heavy lifting she did yesterday.*

fatigue: a feeling of tiredness

- *Because of his fatigue, Ahmet almost fell asleep while he was driving.*

fracture: to break a bone

- *Vladimir fractured his leg when he fell from the scaffold.*

mental problem: an illness or injury that starts in, or affects, the mind; compare to *physical problem* below

- *The doctor said Minh's stomach problems were probably mental in origin.*

numbness: a health or injury problem in which there is no feeling in a part of the body

- *Sofia felt numbness in her hands after working outside in the cold air.*

physical problem: an illness or injury that starts in, or affects, the body; compare to *mental problem* above

- *A complete examination showed that Loni was in good health and had no physical problems.*

puncture: to injure with a sharp point that makes a hole into the body

- *The drill punctured Ken's hand.*

shock: **1.** an injury caused by the sudden passing of electricity through the body

- *The wet plug gave Miriam a bad shock that sent her to the hospital.*

   2. a physical reaction to injury, often with fast heartbeat, change in breathing, and a feeling of weakness and confusion

- *Augusto was still in shock after his accident.*

slip: to fall on a wet or slippery surface

- *Abe slipped on the ice while unloading the truck.*

sprain: to injure a part of the body by turning it suddenly; see *twist* below

- *Soo sprained her wrist while trying to loosen the bolts on the tire.*

strain: to injure a part of the body by pushing or pulling with too much force for too long a time

- *Joe strained a muscle by pulling too hard on a sofa he was moving.*

stress: a feeling of mental pressure caused by too many difficulties in your job or personal life

- *Orly felt a great deal of stress because of language difficulties and money problems.*

tightness: pain in a muscle that becomes stiff and hard from overwork

- *Karl loosened the tightness in his back by taking a hot bath.*

tingle: to feel as if small pinpoints are touching the skin

- *Erica's legs sometimes tingled because she sat in the same position at work all day.*

trip: to fall by catching your foot on something

- *Van tripped over the box that another worker had left in the middle of the floor.*

twist: to hurt a part of the body by turning it sharply; see *sprain* above

- *Gwen twisted her knee when she turned too fast.*

wound: a serious injury that breaks or tears the skin

- *Ian's foot wound was bleeding so badly that he needed stitches to close it.*

Health and Safety Policies

Policies are company rules. Exact policies may differ from company to company, but the problems that the policies deal with are often the same.

Here is a sample of health and safety policies from an employee handbook. Many company policies are similar to these.

Apex Tool Company
Employee Handbook

Health and Safety Policies

Health Policies

Smoking Policy Employees may smoke only in special areas identified by the company. Smoking in all other areas on company property is cause for disciplinary action or referral to corrective action programs.

Drug and Alcohol Policy All use of illegal drugs or alcoholic beverages while on duty is prohibited. Apex may test employees for drug or alcohol use. Employees who test positive will be referred to a corrective action program. Continued violations may result in termination of employment.

Violence Policy The company prohibits all workplace violence to other workers or company property. Violations are cause for disciplinary action or dismissal. No weapons may be carried in the workplace.

HIV/AIDS Policy Apex will not discriminate when hiring or employing people with HIV/AIDS. The company recognizes the need of HIV/AIDS-infected employees for privacy and confidentiality.

Safety Policies

Dress Policy Employees must wear safe clothing on the job. Long-sleeved shirts are prohibited in areas where machines are in operation. No open-toed shoes are permitted.

Personal Protective Equipment (PPE) The company will provide appropriate PPE required for each job. Employees may request alternative equipment if it provides greater protection. Safety glasses and earplugs are mandatory for anyone on the factory floor.

Know Your Limits Employees should not try to do a job or make a repair for which they have not been trained. They can create a danger for themselves, other employees, or Apex visitors.

Safety Committee The company encourages employees to appoint a group that helps to identify and solve workplace safety problems. This Safety Committee will meet regularly with management to discuss the safety concerns of employees.

Reporting Problems Employees should report immediately to their supervisor any accidents or injuries that happen on the job. Any broken equipment or other safety concerns should also be reported to the supervisor. If the problem is not solved, employees should ask to see the department head. If the problem is still not solved, it will be referred to the general manager.

Understanding Workplace Policies

Use the policies on pages 89–90. Check **OK** if the worker's behavior is within company policy. Check **Violation** if the worker is breaking a company policy.

OK   Violation

____   ____   1. Olga has a cigarette in a room labeled *Employee Smoking Area.*

____   ____   2. Mike has two beers with fellow workers at a bar after leaving work.

____   ____   3. Luong wears sandals while packing tools for shipping.

____   ____   4. Chris angrily pushes an older worker who is slowing him down in a hallway.

____   ____   5. Company management dismisses a worker because the worker has tested positive for AIDS.

____   ____   6. Blanca uses a cotton rag to tie off a leak in a water pipe. Then she continues working.

____   ____   7. Van almost falls because a stair railing is loose. He tells his supervisor right away.

____   ____   8. Sara is bothered by the noise from the machinery in her department. She wears earmuffs instead of just earplugs.

____   ____   9. Peggy is a machinist. In the winter she wears heavy, long-sleeved shirts to work in order to be warm enough.

____   ____   10. Marta has some ideas for improving safety in the company. She has volunteered to serve on the Employee Safety Committee.

What Should They Do?

Use the policies on pages 89–90. Check the best answer.

1. Jon sees another worker get hurt in an accident. He should
   _____ **a.** wait until the end of his shift to report it
   _____ **b.** go to his supervisor right away to report the problem

2. The Safety Committee at Apex identifies a work area where slips and falls are common. The committee should
   _____ **a.** warn employees not to work until the problem is fixed
   _____ **b.** bring the problem to the attention of management

3. Al's supervisor unexpectedly gives him an extra machine to work on. In his anger Al hits and breaks the machine. The company should
   _____ **a.** assign Al to work on a different machine
   _____ **b.** discipline Al by fining him or laying him off temporarily

4. Phu is concerned that old wires are wearing out on a machine he uses every day. He should
   _____ **a.** tell his supervisor about the problem and ask for someone to change the wires
   _____ **b.** try to rewire the machine himself

5. Apex knows that Molly drinks whiskey at work. She is a danger to others when she is drunk. She refuses to stop drinking or to see someone who can help. Apex should
   _____ **a.** give Molly a job that is less dangerous to others
   _____ **b.** fire Molly

6. Kay likes to smoke in the Apex parking lot. The company has warned her several times not to do so. Apex should
   _____ **a.** offer Kay a program that will help her stop smoking
   _____ **b.** accept Kay's behavior because she is smoking outside and not inside the company building

TOOL KIT
D
Lockouts and Tagouts (LOTO)

Lockouts and tagouts are very important safety devices in workplaces where machines are used. They help stop injuries around machines that have been shut down for repair or inspection. When a lockout or tagout is on a machine, workers know they must not or cannot turn on that machine.

A lockout is a lock that stops all operation of a machine. Some lockouts stop the electric power that runs a machine. Other lockouts keep the control switch on a machine in the OFF position so that it cannot run. Most lockouts also include a tagout.

A tagout is a tag with a written warning that tells workers not to use a machine that is shut down. Tagouts should be easy to read and easy to see on the machine.

Only employees who are trained in the use of lockouts and tagouts can put them on or remove them. In some companies, only one person is in charge of all lockout/tagout devices. No other employees are permitted to touch them.

Without lockouts and tagouts, many accidents can happen in a workplace. If a machine that has been shut down starts up unexpectedly, it can give a worker a bad burn or electric shock. If a worker turns on a machine that has been shut down, a moving part can hit or pull another worker or repair person who doesn't expect the machine to start up.

Pay careful attention to lockouts and tagouts when you see them on machines. They can save your life!

Lockouts have many shapes in the workplace. Here are some examples.
Remember that most lockouts also come with tags.

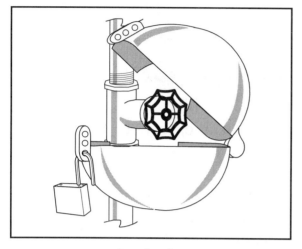

valve lockout

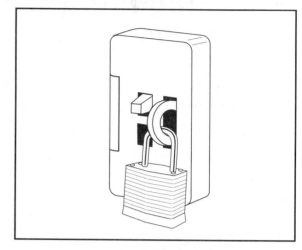

switch lockout

fusebox lockout

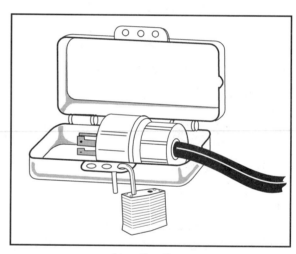

plug lockout

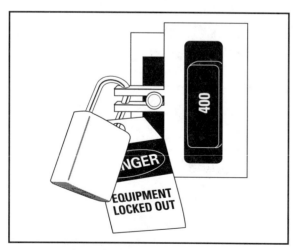

circuit breaker lockout

outlet lockout

What Does It Say?

Check the correct meaning for each tagout.

1.

_____ **a.** Stay away from this machine. It is being repaired.

_____ **b.** Don't touch this machine. It can give you an electric shock.

2.

_____ **a.** Don't move your body too much when you operate this machine.

_____ **b.** Don't push, pull, or lift this machine from where it is now.

3.

_____ **a.** Do not start this machine unless you are trained; you can get hurt.

_____ **b.** Do not turn on this machine while it has this tag; you can get hurt.

4.

_____ **a.** This machine leaks hot water. Keep the pipes closed.

_____ **b.** This machine won't work right. Leave it alone.

5.

_____ **a.** Do not turn this valve. There is hazardous gas in the pipe.

_____ **b.** This equipment is not ready for use.

Use the Right Tagout

Circle the letter of the tagout that says the same thing as each warning.

1. Do not operate this machine. It can hurt you.

a.

b.

2. Don't turn this machine on!

a.

b.

3. Stay out of this area. The machinery is shut down.

a.

b.

4. Don't touch this machine!

a.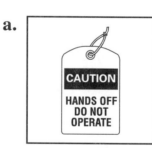

b.

5. This machine still has electric power and can give you a bad shock. Don't touch!

a.

b.

6. This new machine doesn't work. Don't use it until it is fixed or replaced.

a.

b.

7. Do not let any water flow into this machine.

a.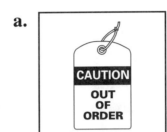

b.

8. Do not use this machine. It is broken.

a.

b.

9. This machine is broken. You must not turn it on until it is fixed.

a.

b.

10. Do not turn on this machine.

a.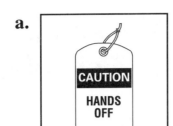

b.

Helpful Exercises for the Workplace

Here are some easy exercises that can help if you start to feel pain in different parts of your body. Try them while you are at work or on a break.

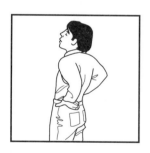

For Hands

Hold both hands up.
Open and close your fingers.
Repeat five times.

For Hands and Wrists

Hold one hand with fingers up.
Push the fingers back with your other hand.
Hold for three seconds.
Repeat five times.

For Lower Back

Put both hands against your lower back.
Bend backward, then straighten your body right away.
Repeat five times.

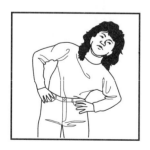

For Back

Put hands on hips.
Stand with feet apart.
Bend at the waist to each side.
Repeat five times.

For Middle and Upper Back

Raise your right arm.

Hold it below the elbow with your left hand.

Gently pull your right elbow toward your left shoulder.

Hold for five seconds.

Do the same with your left arm.

For Neck

Pull your chin into your chest.

Hold for three seconds.

Repeat five times.

For Neck and Shoulders

Bend your head to the right.

Hold for three seconds.

Bend your head to the left.

Hold for three seconds.

Repeat five times.

For Shoulders and Back

Roll your shoulders back five times.

Roll your shoulders forward five times.

For Eyes

Look up from your work.

Look at something far away.

Continue to look for 20 seconds.

Look again at your work.

Answer Key

Unit 1

■ Lesson 1

Which Sign? (page 7)

1. b	6. b
2. a	7. a
3. a	8. b
4. b	9. b
5. b	10. a

What Is the Danger? (page 8)

1. Watch Your Step
2. Keep Area Clean
3. Keep Aisles Clear
4. No Smoking

Work Safely (page 9)

Answers will vary.

■ Lesson 2

What Does It Protect? (page 11)

1. eyes: safety glasses, goggles, face shield
2. head: hard hat, hair net
3. feet: rubber boots, work boots, work shoes, safety shoes
4. lungs: respirator, dust mask
5. ears: earplugs, earmuffs
6. hands: gloves

Protect Yourself (page 11)

1. f	7. d
2. h	8. h
3. k	9. g
4. j, c	10. i
5. b	11. a, e, f
6. a, e	

What Should They Wear? (page 12)

1. work shoes, gloves, goggles
2. work shoes, face shield, hard hat, gloves, earplugs
3. earmuffs, work shoes or work boots, dust mask, gloves
4. gloves, dust mask

Work Safely (page 13)

1. a
2. a
3. b
4. a
5. a

■ Lesson 3

What Should Be There? (page 15)

1. fire escape	6. guardrail
2. fire extinguisher	7. sprinklers
3. eyewash station	8. first aid kit
4. emergency lighting	9. fire alarm
5. security system	

What Is the Danger (page 16)

1. blocked emergency exit
2. empty first aid kit
3. broken guardrail
4. locked exit door

Do's and Don'ts (page 17)

Answers will vary.

■ Lesson 4

What to Use? (page 19)

1. a	6. a
2. b	7. b
3. b	8. b
4. a	9. a
5. a	10. a

Apply First Aid (page 20)

1. syrup of ipecac
2. adhesive bandage
3. hot water bottle
4. eyewash/eyecup

What Does It Do? (page 21)

1. d	8. g
2. k	9. i
3. n	10. e
4. m	11. l
5. a	12. b
6. f	13. j
7. c	14. h

Unit 1 Review (page 22)

1. d
2. b
3. i
4. e
5. a
6. c
7. g
8. h
9. j
10. f

Unit 2

Lesson 5

Which Tool to Use? (page 25)

1. a
2. a
3. a
4. b
5. a
6. b
7. b
8. a
9. b
10. a
11. a

What Are the Dangers? (page 26)

1. b, c, f
2. a, d
3. b, f
4. a, f

Be Safe (page 27)

Answers will vary.

Lesson 6

Do the Job (page 29)

1. b
2. a
3. a
4. b
5. a
6. b
7. b
8. a
9. b
10. a

What Are the Dangers? (page 30)

1. b, f
2. b, d, g
3. c, d, e, g
4. a, e, f

Be Safe (page 30)

Answers will vary.

Lesson 7

What Do They Use? (page 33)

1. bulldozer
2. drill press
3. trash compactor
4. baler
5. sewing machine
6. mower
7. tractor
8. bench sander
9. jackhammer
10. guillotine shears
11. die press

What Is the Danger? (page 34)

1. Wear Safety Glasses, Cover Long Hair
2. Keep Hands Clear, No Loose Clothing
3. Use Ear Protection, Wear Safety Glasses
4. Turn Off before Repair, No Loose Clothing

Know the Risks (page 35)

1. a
2. b
3. b
4. a
5. b

Lesson 8

What Does It Do? (page 37)

1. pedal
2. trigger
3. switch
4. dial
5. nozzle
6. cord
7. blades
8. arm
9. belt and pulley
10. handles

What Is the Danger? (page 38)

1. Take off your bracelet near the belt and pulley.
2. The rollers on that belt are loose.
3. Don't open that! It's still plugged in.
4. Don't turn that on! The cord is frayed.

Replace the Part (page 39)

1. frayed
2. brittle
3. stuck
4. dull

Lesson 9

What Does It Do? (page 41)

1. c
2. a
3. h
4. g
5. i
6. b
7. e
8. d
9. f

Do the Job (page 41)

1. blade guard, pulley guard, gate, body bar
2. lockout guard, safety latch, plate guard
3. cutoff switch, trip wire, electric eye

What Do They Need? (page 42)

1. a
2. b
3. a
4. b
5. b
6. a
7. a

Be Safe (page 43)

1. Never
2. Never
3. Always
4. Always
5. Never
6. Never

▇ Unit 2 Review (page 44)

1. a
2. a
3. b
4. a
5. a
6. b
7. b
8. a
9. handsaw, circular saw, jigsaw, table saw
10. pinking shears, guillotine shears
11. file, sander, bench sander
12. hacksaw, snips, drill press, guillotine shears
13. chisel, jackhammer

Unit 3 ▇▇▇▇▇▇▇▇▇▇▇▇▇▇▇

▇ Lesson 10

Be Safe (page 47)

1. b   6. a
2. b   7. a
3. a   8. b
4. a   9. b
5. b

What Is the Problem? (page 48)

1. standing for long periods, poor ventilation
2. cramped work position, wrong chair for the job, weak lighting, eyestrain, poor workstation design
3. loud noise, poor workstation design
4. repetitive motion, standing for long periods

Health Problems (page 49)

Students may suggest additional problems that fit the situations.

1. a, c, d, i
2. a, e, f, i
3. b, f, h
4. a, d, g

▇ Lesson 11

Do the Job (page 51)

1. a   6. a
2. b   7. a
3. b   8. a
4. a   9. b
5. b   10. a

What Do They Need? (page 52)

1. platform or hand truck or conveyor belt
2. dolly or forklift
3. wheelbarrow or dolly and ramp
4. sling

What's the Risk? (page 53)

1. a, b, possibly d
2. a, b
3. a, b, d, e
4. a, c

▇ Lesson 12

Repeated Movements (page 55)

1. b   6. b
2. b   7. b
3. a   8. a
4. b   9. a
5. a   10. b

Move Safely! (page 56)

1. a
2. b
3. b
4. a
5. b
6. b

Lifting and Carrying (page 57)

1. N   5. Y
2. N   6. N
3. Y   7. Y
4. Y   8. N

◼ Lesson 13

What to Use (page 59)

1. b   6. b
2. a   7. b
3. a   8. a
4. b   9. b
5. a

Do's and Don'ts: Ladders (page 60)

1. 2, 4, 5, 6
2. 7, 8, 9
3. 1, 3, 9

Safety Tips (page 61)

1. steps
2. handrail
3. rope
4. rungs
5. guardrails

◼ Unit 3 Review (page 62)

1. i   6. c
2. d   7. e
3. a   8. g
4. j   9. h
5. f   10. b

Unit 4

◼ Lesson 14

What Is the Danger? (page 65)

1. b
2. b
3. a
4. b
5. a
6. b

What Does It Say? (page 65)

1. Radiation Hazard, Keep Hands Away, Pinch Point, High Voltage, Hot Surface, Rotating Blades
2. Keep Guards in Place, Shut Off before Servicing
3. Do Not Start Equipment, Lockout: Do Not Operate, Do Not Open Valve

What's the Warning? (page 66)

1. Hot Surface, Shut Off before Servicing
2. Keep Hands Away, Keep Guards in Place
3. Pinch Point, Shut Off before Servicing
4. Rotating Blades, Objects May Be Thrown from Machine, Shut Off before Servicing

Tags to Know (page 67)

1. c
2. e
3. b
4. d
5. a

◼ Lesson 15

Be Safe (page 69)

1. b   5. a
2. a   6. a
3. b   7. b
4. a   8. b

Safety Warnings (page 70)

1. b   5. b
2. a   6. a
3. b   7. b
4. b   8. a

Labels and Protective Equipment (page 71)

1. c   5. b
2. d   6. d
3. e   7. a, e
4. a

◼ Lesson 16

What Should They Do? (page 73)

1. b   5. b
2. a   6. b
3. a   7. b
4. a   8. a

Read the Label (page 74)

1. induce vomiting
2. Poison Control Center
3. Flush
4. Wash
5. persists
6. fresh air
7. artificial respiration

Safety Checkup (page 75)

1. F
2. F
3. T
4. F
5. T
6. T

◼ Lesson 17

What Is the Warning? (page 77)

1. b		6. a	
2. a		7. b	
3. a		8. a	
4. b		9. b	
5. b		10. b	

Follow Instructions (page 78)

1. Do Not Discard in Trash
2. Keep Container Tightly Closed
3. Do Not Store near Food
4. Do Not Incinerate

Be Safe (page 79)

1. b
2. b
3. a
4. a

◼ Unit 4 Review (page 80)

Answers will vary.

Safety Tool Kit

◼ Tool Kit A

Using an MSDS (page 85)

1. b
2. a
3. b
4. b
5. b
6. a

◼ Tool Kit C

Understanding Workplace Policies (page 91)

1. OK	6. Violation
2. OK	7. OK
3. Violation	8. OK
4. Violation	9. Violation
5. Violation	10. OK

What Should They Do? (page 92)

1. b
2. b
3. b
4. a
5. b
6. a

◼ Tool Kit D

What Does It Say? (page 95)

1. a
2. b
3. b
4. b
5. a

Use the Right Tagout (page 96)

1. b	6. b
2. b	7. a
3. a	8. a
4. a	9. a
5. b	10. a

Key Word List

My Word List

Use these blank pages to write down other safety terms you learn. They can be terms used at your workplace or other safety terms you want to remember.

_____

_____

_____

_____

_____

_____

_____

_____

_____

_____

_____